This Journal Belongs To

D1318344

📍Location_____ 🗓Date_____

Weather :☀ ⛅ ☁ ⚡ 🌧 ❄
_____
_____

What I did today
_____
_____
_____
_____
_____

Best thing that happened today
_____
_____
_____

Funniest thing that happened today
_____
_____
_____

My mood was : 😊 😍 😎 😜 😴 😣
_____
_____

Who I shared the day with
_____
_____
_____

Today I am grateful for
_____
_____
_____

📍Location_____ 📅 Date_____

Weather : ☀️ ⛅ ☁️ ⛈️ 🌧️ 🌨️
_____
_____

What I did today

_____
_____
_____
_____
_____
_____

Best thing that happened today

_____
_____
_____

Funniest thing that happened today

_____
_____
_____

My mood was : 😊 😍 😎 😜 😤 😣

_____
_____

Who I shared the day with

_____
_____
_____

Today I am grateful for

_____
_____
_____

Location_____ 📅 Date_____

Weather :- ☀️ ⛅ ☁️ ⛈️ 🌧️ 🌨️
_____
_____

What I did today
_____
_____
_____
_____
_____
_____
_____

Best thing that happened today
_____
_____
_____
_____

Funniest thing that happened today
_____
_____
_____
_____

My mood was : 😊 😍 😎 😜 😴 😭
_____
_____

Who I shared the day with
_____
_____
_____

Today I am grateful for
_____
_____
_____

📍Location_____ 📅 Date_____

Weather :- ☀️ 🌤️ ☁️ ⚡ 🌧️ 🌨️
_____
_____

What I did today

_____
_____
_____
_____
_____

Best thing that happened today

_____
_____
_____

Funniest thing that happened today

_____
_____
_____

My mood was : 😊 😍 😎 😋 😴 😣

_____
_____

Who I shared the day with

_____
_____
_____

Today I am grateful for

_____
_____
_____

📍Location_____ 📅 Date_____

Weather : ☀️ ⛅ ☁️ ⛈️ 🌧️ 🌨️
_____
_____

What I did today
_____
_____
_____
_____
_____
_____

Best thing that happened today
_____
_____
_____
_____

Funniest thing that happened today
_____
_____
_____
_____

My mood was : 😊 😍 😎 😜 😤 😢
_____
_____

Who I shared the day with
_____
_____
_____

Today I am grateful for
_____
_____
_____

Location_____ :::: Date_____

Weather : ☀ ⛅ ☁ ⛈ 🌧 🌨
_____
_____

What I did today
_____
_____
_____
_____
_____
_____

Best thing that happened today
_____
_____
_____

Funniest thing that happened today
_____
_____
_____

My mood was : 😊 😍 😎 😜 😤 😢
_____
_____

Who I shared the day with
_____
_____
_____

Today I am grateful for
_____
_____
_____

📍Location_____ 📅 Date_____

Weather : ☀️ ⛅ ☁️ ⛈️ 🌧️ 🌨️
_____
_____

What I did today
_____
_____
_____
_____
_____
_____
_____

Best thing that happened today
_____
_____
_____
_____
_____

Funniest thing that happened today
_____
_____
_____
_____
_____

My mood was : 😊 😍 😎 😜 😴 😭
_____
_____

Who I shared the day with
_____
_____
_____

Today I am grateful for
_____
_____
_____

📍Location_____ 🗓Date_____

Weather : ☀️ ⛅ ☁️ ⚡ 🌧 🌨

_____
_____

What I did today

_____
_____
_____
_____
_____

Best thing that happened today

_____
_____
_____
_____

Funniest thing that happened today

_____
_____
_____
_____

My mood was : 😊 😍 😎 😜 😴 😣

_____
_____

Who I shared the day with

_____
_____
_____

Today I am grateful for

_____
_____
_____

◉ Location_____ 🗓 Date_____

Weather :☀ ⛅ ☁ ⛈ 🌧 🌨
_____
_____

What I did today
_____
_____
_____
_____
_____

Best thing that happened today
_____
_____
_____
_____

Funniest thing that happened today
_____
_____
_____
_____

My mood was : 😊 😍 😎 😜 😴 😖
_____
_____

Who I shared the day with
_____
_____
_____

Today I am grateful for
_____
_____
_____

📍Location_____ 🗓Date_____

Weather : ☀️ ⛅ ☁️ ⛈️ 🌧️ 🌨️
_____
_____

What I did today
_____
_____
_____
_____
_____
_____
_____

Best thing that happened today
_____
_____
_____
_____

Funniest thing that happened today
_____
_____
_____
_____

My mood was : 😊 😍 😎 😜 😴 😢
_____
_____

Who I shared the day with
_____
_____
_____

Today I am grateful for
_____
_____
_____

📍Location_____ 🗓️Date_____

Weather :☀️ 🌤️ ☁️ ⚡ 🌧️ ❄️
_____
_____

What I did today
_____
_____
_____
_____
_____
_____
_____

Best thing that happened today
_____
_____
_____
_____

Funniest thing that happened today
_____
_____
_____
_____

My mood was : 😊 😍 😎 😜 😴 😢
_____
_____

Who I shared the day with
_____
_____
_____

Today I am grateful for
_____
_____
_____

📍Location_____ 📅 Date_____

Weather : ☀️ ⛅ ☁️ ⛈️ 🌧️ 🌨️
_____
_____

What I did today
_____
_____
_____
_____
_____
_____

Best thing that happened today
_____
_____
_____
_____

Funniest thing that happened today
_____
_____
_____
_____

My mood was : 😊 😍 😎 😜 😤 😭
_____
_____

Who I shared the day with
_____
_____
_____

Today I am grateful for
_____
_____
_____

📍Location_____ 📅Date_____

Weather :☀️ ⛅ ☁️ ⛈️ 🌧️ 🌨️
_____
_____

What I did today

_____
_____
_____
_____
_____
_____
_____

Best thing that happened today

_____
_____
_____
_____

Funniest thing that happened today

_____
_____
_____
_____

My mood was : 😊 😍 😎 😜 😴 😣

_____
_____

Who I shared the day with

_____
_____
_____

Today I am grateful for

_____
_____
_____

📍Location_____ 📅 Date_____

Weather :☀️ ⛅ ☁️ ⛈️ 🌧️ 🌨️
_____
_____

What I did today
_____
_____
_____
_____
_____
_____

Best thing that happened today
_____
_____
_____
_____

Funniest thing that happened today
_____
_____
_____
_____

My mood was : 😊 😍 😎 😜 😤 😢
_____
_____

Who I shared the day with
_____
_____
_____
_____

Today I am grateful for
_____
_____
_____
_____

📍Location_____ 🗓Date_____

Weather :- ☀ ⛅ ☁ ⛈ 🌧 🌨
_____
_____

What I did today
_____
_____
_____
_____
_____
_____

Best thing that happened today
_____
_____
_____
_____

Funniest thing that happened today
_____
_____
_____
_____

My mood was : 😊 😍 😎 😜 😪 😭
_____
_____

Who I shared the day with
_____
_____
_____

Today I am grateful for
_____
_____
_____

◉ Location_____ 📅 Date_____

Weather :- ☀ ⛅ ☁ ⛈ 🌧 🌨
_____
_____

What I did today
_____
_____
_____
_____
_____
_____

Best thing that happened today
_____
_____
_____
_____

Funniest thing that happened today
_____
_____
_____
_____

My mood was : 😊 😍 😎 😜 😴 😢
_____
_____

Who I shared the day with
_____
_____
_____

Today I am grateful for
_____
_____
_____

📍Location_____ 📅 Date_____

Weather :-☀️ ⛅ ☁️ ⛈️ 🌧️ 🌨️
_____
_____

What I did today
_____
_____
_____
_____
_____
_____

Best thing that happened today
_____
_____
_____
_____

Funniest thing that happened today
_____
_____
_____
_____

My mood was : 😊 😍 😎 😛 😴 😢
_____
_____

Who I shared the day with
_____
_____
_____

Today I am grateful for
_____
_____
_____

📍Location_____ 📅Date_____

Weather :☀️ ⛅ ☁️ ⛈️ 🌧️ 🌨️
_____
_____

What I did today
_____
_____
_____
_____
_____
_____

Best thing that happened today
_____
_____
_____
_____

Funniest thing that happened today
_____
_____
_____
_____

My mood was : 😊 😍 😎 😜 😤 😣
_____
_____

Who I shared the day with
_____
_____
_____
_____

Today I am grateful for
_____
_____
_____
_____

📍Location_____ 📅 Date_____

Weather :☀️ ⛅ ☁️ ⛈️ 🌧️ 🌨️
_____
_____

What I did today
_____
_____
_____
_____
_____
_____

Best thing that happened today
_____
_____
_____
_____

Funniest thing that happened today
_____
_____
_____
_____

My mood was : 😊 😍 😎 😜 😤 😢
_____
_____

Who I shared the day with
_____
_____
_____

Today I am grateful for
_____
_____
_____

📍Location_____ 📅 Date_____

Weather : ☀ ⛅ ☁ ⛈ 🌧 🌨
_____
_____

What I did today
_____
_____
_____
_____
_____
_____
_____

Best thing that happened today
_____
_____
_____
_____
_____

Funniest thing that happened today
_____
_____
_____
_____
_____

My mood was : 😊 😍 😎 😜 😤 😣
_____
_____

Who I shared the day with
_____
_____
_____
_____

Today I am grateful for
_____
_____
_____

📍Location_____ 🗓Date_____

Weather : ☀ ⛅ ☁ ⚡ 🌧 ❄
_____
_____

What I did today
_____
_____
_____
_____
_____
_____

Best thing that happened today
_____
_____
_____
_____

Funniest thing that happened today
_____
_____
_____
_____

My mood was : 😊 😍 😎 😜 😴 😫
_____
_____

Who I shared the day with
_____
_____
_____

Today I am grateful for
_____
_____
_____

Location_____ **Date**_____

Weather :

What I did today
_____
_____
_____
_____
_____
_____

Best thing that
happened today
_____
_____
_____
_____

Funniest thing that
happened today
_____
_____
_____
_____

My mood was :
_____

Who I shared the
day with
_____
_____
_____

Today I am grateful for
_____
_____
_____

📍 Location_____ 📅 Date_____

Weather : ☀️ ⛅ ☁️ ⛈️ 🌧️ 🌨️
_____
_____

What I did today
_____
_____
_____
_____
_____
_____

Best thing that happened today
_____
_____
_____
_____

Funniest thing that happened today
_____
_____
_____
_____

My mood was : 😊 😍 😎 😜 😴 😢
_____
_____

Who I shared the day with
_____
_____
_____
_____

Today I am grateful for
_____
_____
_____
_____

📍Location_____ 📅 Date_____

Weather :☀ ⛅ ☁ ⛈ 🌧 🌨
_____
_____

What I did today
_____
_____
_____
_____
_____
_____

Best thing that happened today
_____
_____
_____
_____

Funniest thing that happened today
_____
_____
_____
_____

My mood was : 😊 😍 😎 😜 😤 😢
_____
_____

Who I shared the day with
_____
_____
_____

Today I am grateful for
_____
_____
_____

📍Location_____ 📅 Date_____

Weather : ☀️ ⛅ ☁️ ⛈️ 🌧️ 🌨️
_____
_____

What I did today
_____
_____
_____
_____
_____
_____
_____

Best thing that happened today
_____
_____
_____
_____

Funniest thing that happened today
_____
_____
_____
_____

My mood was : 😊 😍 😎 😜 😒 😣
_____
_____

Who I shared the day with
_____
_____
_____

Today I am grateful for
_____
_____
_____

📍 Location_____ 📅 Date_____

Weather :: ☀ ⛅ ☁ ⛈ 🌧 🌨
_____
_____

What I did today
_____
_____
_____
_____
_____
_____

Best thing that happened today
_____
_____
_____
_____

Funniest thing that happened today
_____
_____
_____
_____

My mood was : 😊 😍 😎 😜 😤 😢
_____
_____

Who I shared the day with
_____
_____
_____
_____

Today I am grateful for
_____
_____
_____

📍Location_____ 📅 Date_____

Weather :- ☀️ 🌤️ ☁️ ⛈️ 🌧️ 🌨️
_____
_____

What I did today
_____
_____
_____
_____
_____
_____

Best thing that happened today
_____
_____
_____
_____

Funniest thing that happened today
_____
_____
_____
_____

My mood was : 😊 😍 😎 😜 😴 😫
_____
_____

Who I shared the day with
_____
_____
_____

Today I am grateful for
_____
_____
_____

📍Location_____ 📅 Date_____

Weather :☀️ ⛅ ☁️ ⛈️ 🌧️ 🌨️
_____
_____

What I did today
_____
_____
_____
_____
_____
_____

Best thing that happened today
_____
_____
_____
_____

Funniest thing that happened today
_____
_____
_____
_____

My mood was : 😊 😍 😎 😝 😤 😢
_____
_____

Who I shared the day with
_____
_____
_____

Today I am grateful for
_____
_____
_____

Location_____ 📅 Date_____

Weather :☀️ ⛅ ☁️ ⛈️ 🌧️ 🌨️
_____
_____

What I did today
_____
_____
_____
_____
_____
_____

Best thing that happened today
_____
_____
_____
_____

Funniest thing that happened today
_____
_____
_____
_____

My mood was : 😊 😍 😎 😜 😤 😩
_____
_____

Who I shared the day with
_____
_____
_____

Today I am grateful for
_____
_____
_____

Location_____ 📅 Date_____

Weather : ☀️ ⛅ ☁️ ⚡ 🌧️ 🌨️
_____
_____

What I did today
_____
_____
_____
_____
_____

Best thing that happened today
_____
_____
_____
_____

Funniest thing that happened today
_____
_____
_____
_____

My mood was : 😊 😍 😎 😜 😪 😣
_____
_____

Who I shared the day with
_____
_____
_____
_____

Today I am grateful for
_____
_____
_____
_____

📍Location_____ 📅 Date_____

Weather :-☀️ ⛅ ☁️ ⛈️ 🌧️ 🌨️
_____
_____

What I did today
_____
_____
_____
_____
_____
_____

Best thing that happened today
_____
_____
_____
_____

Funniest thing that happened today
_____
_____
_____
_____

My mood was : 😊 😍 😎 😜 😒 😣
_____
_____

Who I shared the day with
_____
_____
_____

Today I am grateful for
_____
_____
_____

📍Location_____ 📅Date_____

Weather :☀️ ⛅ ☁️ ⛈️ 🌧️ 🌨️
_____
_____

What I did today

_____
_____
_____
_____
_____
_____

Best thing that happened today

_____
_____
_____
_____

Funniest thing that happened today

_____
_____
_____
_____

My mood was : 😊 😍 😎 😜 😤 😩

_____
_____

Who I shared the day with

_____
_____
_____

Today I am grateful for

_____
_____
_____

📍Location_____ 📅Date_____

Weather :☀️ 🌤️ ☁️ ⚡ 🌧️ 🌨️

_____
_____

What I did today

_____
_____
_____
_____
_____

Best thing that happened today

_____
_____
_____
_____

Funniest thing that happened today

_____
_____
_____
_____

My mood was : 😊 😍 😎 😜 😴 😭

_____
_____

Who I shared the day with

_____
_____
_____

Today I am grateful for

_____
_____
_____

◍ Location_____ ▦ Date_____

Weather :: ☀ ⛅ ☁ ⚡ 🌧 ❄
_____
_____

What I did today
_____
_____
_____
_____
_____
_____

Best thing that happened today
_____
_____
_____
_____
_____

Funniest thing that happened today
_____
_____
_____
_____
_____

My mood was : 😊 😍 😎 😉 😤 😩

_____
_____

Who I shared the day with
_____
_____
_____
_____

Today I am grateful for
_____
_____
_____
_____

📍Location_____ 📅Date_____

Weather :☀️ 🌤️ ☁️ ⛈️ 🌧️ 🌨️
_____
_____

What I did today
_____
_____
_____
_____
_____
_____
_____

Best thing that happened today
_____
_____
_____
_____

Funniest thing that happened today
_____
_____
_____
_____

My mood was : 😊 😍 😎 😜 😤 😫
_____
_____

Who I shared the day with
_____
_____
_____

Today I am grateful for
_____
_____
_____

📍Location_____ 📅 Date_____

Weather :☀️ ⛅ ☁️ ⛈️ 🌧️ 🌨️
_____
_____

What I did today
_____
_____
_____
_____
_____
_____

Best thing that happened today
_____
_____
_____
_____

Funniest thing that happened today
_____
_____
_____
_____

My mood was : 😊 😍 😎 😜 😠 😢
_____
_____

Who I shared the day with
_____
_____
_____

Today I am grateful for
_____
_____
_____

📍Location_____ 🗓Date_____

Weather :☀ ⛅ ☁ ⛈ 🌧 🌨
_____
_____

What I did today
_____
_____
_____
_____
_____
_____

Best thing that happened today
_____
_____
_____
_____

Funniest thing that happened today
_____
_____
_____
_____

My mood was : 😊 😍 😎 😜 😒 😭
_____
_____

Who I shared the day with
_____
_____
_____

Today I am grateful for
_____
_____
_____

📍Location_____ 📅 Date_____

Weather :- ☀️ ⛅ ☁️ ⛈️ 🌧️ 🌨️
_____
_____

What I did today

_____
_____
_____
_____
_____
_____

Best thing that happened today

_____
_____
_____
_____

Funniest thing that happened today

_____
_____
_____
_____

My mood was : 😊 😍 😎 😜 😤 😣

_____
_____

Who I shared the day with

_____
_____
_____

Today I am grateful for

_____
_____
_____

📍Location_____ 📅 Date_____

Weather :☀️ ⛅ ☁️ ⛈️ 🌧️ 🌨️
_____
_____

What I did today
_____
_____
_____
_____
_____
_____

Best thing that happened today
_____
_____
_____

Funniest thing that happened today
_____
_____
_____

My mood was : 😊 😍 😎 😜 😴 😢
_____
_____

Who I shared the day with
_____
_____
_____

Today I am grateful for
_____
_____
_____

📍Location_____ 📅 Date_____

Weather :☀️ ⛅ ☁️ ⛈️ 🌧️ 🌨️
_____
_____

What I did today
_____
_____
_____
_____
_____
_____

Best thing that happened today
_____
_____
_____
_____

Funniest thing that happened today
_____
_____
_____
_____

My mood was : 😊 😍 😎 😜 😠 😢
_____
_____

Who I shared the day with
_____
_____
_____

Today I am grateful for
_____
_____
_____

📍Location_____ 📅Date_____

Weather :☀️ ⛅ ☁️ ⚡ 🌧️ 🌨️
_____
_____

What I did today
_____
_____
_____
_____
_____

Best thing that happened today
_____
_____
_____

Funniest thing that happened today
_____
_____
_____

My mood was : 😊 😍 😎 😜 😴 😣
_____
_____

Who I shared the day with
_____
_____
_____

Today I am grateful for
_____
_____
_____

📍Location_____ 🗓️ Date_____

Weather :☀️ ⛅ ☁️ ⛈️ 🌧️ 🌨️
_____
_____

What I did today
_____
_____
_____
_____
_____
_____

Best thing that happened today
_____
_____
_____
_____

Funniest thing that happened today
_____
_____
_____
_____

My mood was : 😊 😍 😎 😛 😤 😫

_____
_____

Who I shared the day with
_____
_____
_____
_____

Today I am grateful for
_____
_____
_____
_____

Location _____ **Date** _____

Weather : ☀ ⛅ ☁ ⛈ 🌧 🌨
_____
_____

What I did today
_____
_____
_____
_____
_____
_____

Best thing that happened today
_____
_____
_____
_____

Funniest thing that happened today
_____
_____
_____
_____

My mood was : 😊 😍 😎 😜 😴 😭
_____
_____

Who I shared the day with
_____
_____
_____

Today I am grateful for
_____
_____
_____

📍Location_____ 🗓Date_____

Weather :: ☀ ⛅ ☁ ⛈ 🌧 🌨
_____
_____

What I did today
_____
_____
_____
_____
_____
_____
_____

Best thing that happened today
_____
_____
_____
_____

Funniest thing that happened today
_____
_____
_____
_____

My mood was : 😊 😍 😎 😋 😠 😢
_____
_____

Who I shared the day with
_____
_____
_____

Today I am grateful for
_____
_____
_____

📍Location_____ 📅 Date_____

Weather : ☀️ ⛅ ☁️ ⚡ 🌧️ 🌨️
_____
_____

What I did today

_____
_____
_____
_____
_____
_____

Best thing that happened today

_____
_____
_____
_____

Funniest thing that happened today

_____
_____
_____
_____

My mood was : 😊 😍 😎 😜 😴 😫
_____
_____

Who I shared the day with

_____
_____
_____

Today I am grateful for

_____
_____
_____

📍Location_____ 🗓️ Date_____

Weather : ☀️ ⛅ ☁️ ⛈️ 🌧️ 🌨️
_____
_____

What I did today
_____
_____
_____
_____
_____
_____

Best thing that happened today
_____
_____
_____
_____

Funniest thing that happened today
_____
_____
_____
_____

My mood was : 😊 😍 😎 😋 😤 😢

_____
_____

Who I shared the day with
_____
_____
_____

Today I am grateful for
_____
_____
_____

📍Location_____ 📅Date_____

Weather : ☀️ ⛅ ☁️ ⛈️ 🌧️ 🌨️
_____
_____

What I did today
_____
_____
_____
_____
_____

Best thing that happened today
_____
_____
_____

Funniest thing that happened today
_____
_____
_____

My mood was : 😊 😍 😎 😜 😴 😭
_____
_____

Who I shared the day with
_____
_____
_____

Today I am grateful for
_____
_____
_____

📍Location_____ 📅 Date_____

Weather :☀️ 🌤️ ☁️ ⛈️ 🌧️ 🌨️
_____
_____

What I did today

_____
_____
_____
_____
_____
_____

Best thing that happened today

_____
_____
_____
_____

Funniest thing that happened today

_____
_____
_____
_____

My mood was : 😊 😍 😎 😜 😠 😢
_____
_____

Who I shared the day with

_____
_____
_____

Today I am grateful for

_____
_____
_____

📍Location_____ 📅Date_____

Weather :☀️ ⛅ ☁️ ⚡ 🌧️ 🌨️
_____
_____

What I did today
_____
_____
_____
_____
_____

Best thing that happened today
_____
_____
_____

Funniest thing that happened today
_____
_____
_____

My mood was : 😊 😍 😎 🤪 😴 😢
_____
_____

Who I shared the day with
_____
_____
_____

Today I am grateful for
_____
_____
_____

📍Location_____ 📅 Date_____

Weather : ☀️ ⛅ ☁️ ⛈️ 🌧️ 🌨️
_____
_____

What I did today

_____
_____
_____
_____
_____

Best thing that happened today

_____
_____
_____
_____

Funniest thing that happened today

_____
_____
_____
_____

My mood was : 😊 😍 😎 😜 😪 😣

_____
_____

Who I shared the day with

_____
_____
_____

Today I am grateful for

_____
_____
_____

📍Location_____ 📅Date_____

Weather :☀️ ⛅ ☁️ ⛈️ 🌧️ 🌨️

_____
_____

What I did today

_____
_____
_____
_____
_____
_____

Best thing that happened today

_____
_____
_____
_____

Funniest thing that happened today

_____
_____
_____
_____

My mood was : 😊 😍 😎 😜 😒 😭

_____
_____

Who I shared the day with

_____
_____
_____

Today I am grateful for

_____
_____
_____

📍Location_____ 📅Date_____

Weather :☀️ ⛅ ☁️ ⛈️ 🌧️ 🌨️
_____
_____

What I did today

_____
_____
_____
_____
_____

Best thing that happened today

_____
_____
_____
_____

Funniest thing that happened today

_____
_____
_____
_____

My mood was : 😊 😍 😎 😜 😴 😢

_____
_____

Who I shared the day with

_____
_____
_____
_____

Today I am grateful for

_____
_____
_____
_____

📍Location_____ 📅Date_____

Weather :- ☀️ ⛅ ☁️ ⚡ 🌧️ 🌨️

_____
_____

What I did today

_____
_____
_____
_____
_____

Best thing that happened today

_____
_____
_____
_____

Funniest thing that happened today

_____
_____
_____
_____

My mood was : 😊 😍 😎 😜 😴 😭

_____
_____

Who I shared the day with

_____
_____
_____

Today I am grateful for

_____
_____
_____

📍Location_____ 🗓️Date_____

Weather : ☀️ ⛅ ☁️ ⚡ 🌧️ 🌨️
_____
_____

What I did today
_____
_____
_____
_____
_____

Best thing that happened today
_____
_____
_____

Funniest thing that happened today
_____
_____
_____

My mood was : 😊 😍 😎 😜 😴 😣
_____
_____

Who I shared the day with
_____
_____
_____

Today I am grateful for
_____
_____
_____

📍Location_____ 📅 Date_____

Weather :☀️ ⛅ ☁️ ⛈️ 🌧️ 🌨️
_____
_____

What I did today
_____
_____
_____
_____
_____
_____

Best thing that happened today
_____
_____
_____
_____

Funniest thing that happened today
_____
_____
_____
_____

My mood was : 😊 😍 😎 😜 😴 😢
_____
_____

Who I shared the day with
_____
_____
_____
_____

Today I am grateful for
_____
_____
_____
_____

Location_____ 📅 Date_____

Weather : ☀️ ⛅ ☁️ ⛈️ 🌧️ 🌨️
_____
_____

What I did today

_____
_____
_____
_____
_____
_____
_____

Best thing that happened today

_____
_____
_____
_____

Funniest thing that happened today

_____
_____
_____
_____

My mood was : 😊 😍 😎 😜 😤 😣

_____
_____

Who I shared the day with

_____
_____
_____

Today I am grateful for

_____
_____
_____

◉ Location_____ 📅 Date_____

Weather : ☀️ ⛅ ☁️ ⛈️ 🌧️ 🌨️
_____
_____

What I did today
_____
_____
_____
_____
_____
_____
_____

Best thing that happened today
_____
_____
_____
_____

Funniest thing that happened today
_____
_____
_____
_____

My mood was : 😊 😍 😎 😜 😴 😭
_____
_____

Who I shared the day with
_____
_____
_____

Today I am grateful for
_____
_____
_____

📍Location_____ 📅 Date_____

Weather : ☀️ 🌤️ ☁️ ⛈️ 🌧️ 🌨️
_____
_____

What I did today

_____
_____
_____
_____
_____
_____

Best thing that happened today

_____
_____
_____
_____

Funniest thing that happened today

_____
_____
_____
_____

My mood was : 😊 😍 😎 😜 😤 😣

_____
_____

Who I shared the day with

_____
_____
_____

Today I am grateful for

_____
_____
_____

📍Location_____ 📅Date_____

Weather : ☀️ 🌤️ ☁️ ⛈️ 🌧️ 🌨️
_____
_____

What I did today
_____
_____
_____
_____
_____
_____

Best thing that happened today
_____
_____
_____
_____

Funniest thing that happened today
_____
_____
_____
_____

My mood was : 😊 😍 😎 😜 😤 😣
_____
_____

Who I shared the day with
_____
_____
_____

Today I am grateful for
_____
_____
_____

📍Location_____ 📅 Date_____

Weather :☀️ 🌤️ ☁️ ⚡ 🌧️ ❄️
_____
_____

What I did today

_____
_____
_____
_____
_____

Best thing that happened today

_____
_____
_____

Funniest thing that happened today

_____
_____
_____

My mood was : 😊 😍 😎 😜 😴 😫

_____
_____

Who I shared the day with

_____
_____
_____

Today I am grateful for

_____
_____
_____

📍Location_____ 📅 Date_____

Weather : ☀️ ⛅ ☁️ ⛈️ 🌧️ 🌨️
_____
_____

What I did today
_____
_____
_____
_____
_____
_____

Best thing that happened today
_____
_____
_____
_____

Funniest thing that happened today
_____
_____
_____
_____

My mood was : 😊 😍 😎 😜 😴 😭
_____
_____

Who I shared the day with
_____
_____
_____

Today I am grateful for
_____
_____
_____

📍Location_____ 📅 Date_____

Weather :- ☀️ 🌤️ ☁️ ⛈️ 🌧️ 🌨️
_____
_____

What I did today
_____
_____
_____
_____
_____
_____

Best thing that happened today
_____
_____
_____
_____

Funniest thing that happened today
_____
_____
_____
_____

My mood was : 😊 😍 😎 😜 😤 😣
_____
_____

Who I shared the day with
_____
_____
_____

Today I am grateful for
_____
_____
_____

📍Location_____ 📅 Date_____

Weather : ☀️ ⛅ ☁️ ⛈️ 🌧️ 🌨️
_____
_____

What I did today
_____
_____
_____
_____
_____
_____

Best thing that happened today
_____
_____
_____
_____

Funniest thing that happened today
_____
_____
_____
_____

My mood was : 😊 😍 😎 😝 😴 😫
_____
_____

Who I shared the day with
_____
_____
_____

Today I am grateful for
_____
_____
_____

📍Location_____ 🗓️ Date_____

Weather :☀️ 🌤️ ☁️ ⛈️ 🌧️ ❄️
_____
_____

What I did today
_____
_____
_____
_____
_____
_____
_____

Best thing that happened today
_____
_____
_____
_____

Funniest thing that happened today
_____
_____
_____
_____

My mood was : 😊 😍 😎 😜 😤 😣
_____

Who I shared the day with
_____
_____
_____

Today I am grateful for
_____
_____
_____

📍Location_____ 🗓️Date_____

Weather : ☀️ ⛅ ☁️ ⛈️ 🌧️ 🌨️
_____
_____

What I did today
_____
_____
_____
_____
_____
_____

Best thing that happened today
_____
_____
_____
_____

Funniest thing that happened today
_____
_____
_____
_____

My mood was : 😊 😍 😎 😜 😴 😭
_____
_____

Who I shared the day with
_____
_____
_____

Today I am grateful for
_____
_____
_____

📍 Location_____ 📅 Date_____

Weather : ☀️ ⛅ ☁️ ⚡ 🌧️ ❄️
_____
_____
_____

What I did today

_____
_____
_____
_____
_____
_____

Best thing that happened today

_____
_____
_____
_____

Funniest thing that happened today

_____
_____
_____
_____

My mood was : 😊 😍 😎 😋 😪 😫

_____
_____

Who I shared the day with

_____
_____
_____

Today I am grateful for

_____
_____
_____

📍Location_____ 🗓 Date_____

Weather : ☀ ⛅ ☁ ⛈ 🌧 🌨
_____
_____

What I did today
_____
_____
_____
_____
_____
_____

Best thing that happened today
_____
_____
_____
_____
_____

Funniest thing that happened today
_____
_____
_____
_____
_____

My mood was : 😊 😍 😎 😜 😴 😣
_____
_____

Who I shared the day with
_____
_____
_____
_____

Today I am grateful for
_____
_____
_____
_____

📍Location_____ 🗓Date_____

Weather :☀ ⛅ ☁ ⚡ 🌧 🌨
_____
_____

What I did today

_____
_____
_____
_____
_____

Best thing that happened today

_____
_____
_____
_____

Funniest thing that happened today

_____
_____
_____
_____

My mood was : 😊 😍 😎 😉 😤 😣

_____
_____

Who I shared the day with

_____
_____
_____

Today I am grateful for

_____
_____
_____

📍Location_____ 📅Date_____

Weather :☀️ ⛅ ☁️ ⚡ 🌧️ 🌨️
_____
_____

What I did today

_____
_____
_____
_____
_____
_____

Best thing that happened today

_____
_____
_____
_____

Funniest thing that happened today

_____
_____
_____
_____

My mood was : 😊 😍 😎 😜 😴 😭

_____
_____

Who I shared the day with

_____
_____
_____

Today I am grateful for

_____
_____
_____

📍Location_____ 📅 Date_____

Weather :☀️ ⛅ ☁️ ⛈️ 🌧️ ❄️
_____
_____

What I did today

_____
_____
_____
_____
_____
_____

Best thing that happened today

_____
_____
_____

Funniest thing that happened today

_____
_____
_____

My mood was : 😊 😍 😎 😜 😴 😢

_____
_____

Who I shared the day with

_____
_____
_____

Today I am grateful for

_____
_____
_____

📍Location_____ 📅Date_____

Weather :☀️ ⛅ ☁️ ⚡ 🌧️ 🌨️

What I did today

Best thing that happened today

Funniest thing that happened today

My mood was : 😊 😍 😎 😜 😴 😫

Who I shared the day with

Today I am grateful for

📍Location_____ 📅Date_____

Weather : ☀️ ⛅ ☁️ ⚡ 🌧️ 🌨️
_____
_____

What I did today
_____
_____
_____
_____
_____

Best thing that happened today
_____
_____
_____
_____

Funniest thing that happened today
_____
_____
_____
_____

My mood was : 😊 😍 😎 😒 😴 😢
_____
_____

Who I shared the day with
_____
_____
_____

Today I am grateful for
_____
_____
_____

📍Location_____ 📅 Date_____

Weather : ☀️ 🌤️ ☁️ ⛈️ 🌧️ 🌨️
_____
_____

What I did today

_____
_____
_____
_____
_____
_____

Best thing that happened today

_____
_____
_____
_____

Funniest thing that happened today

_____
_____
_____
_____

My mood was : 😊 😍 😎 😜 😴 😫

_____
_____

Who I shared the day with

_____
_____
_____

Today I am grateful for

_____
_____
_____

📍Location_____ 📅 Date_____

Weather : ☀️ ⛅ ☁️ ⛈️ 🌧️ 🌨️
_____
_____

What I did today

_____
_____
_____
_____
_____
_____
_____

Best thing that happened today

_____
_____
_____
_____
_____

Funniest thing that happened today

_____
_____
_____
_____
_____

My mood was : 😊 😍 😎 😜 😴 😣

_____
_____

Who I shared the day with

_____
_____
_____
_____

Today I am grateful for

_____
_____
_____
_____

📍Location_____   📅 Date_____

Weather ::☀️ ⛅ ☁️ ⛈️ 🌧️ 🌨️
_____
_____

What I did today
_____
_____
_____
_____
_____

Best thing that happened today
_____
_____
_____
_____

Funniest thing that happened today
_____
_____
_____
_____

My mood was : 😊 😍 😎 😜 😒 😭
_____
_____

Who I shared the day with
_____
_____
_____

Today I am grateful for
_____
_____
_____

📍Location_____ 📅 Date_____

Weather : ☀️ ⛅ ☁️ ⚡ 🌧️ 🌨️
_____
_____

What I did today

_____
_____
_____
_____
_____
_____

Best thing that happened today
_____
_____
_____
_____

Funniest thing that happened today
_____
_____
_____
_____

My mood was : 😊 😍 😎 😋 😴 😣
_____
_____

Who I shared the day with
_____
_____
_____
_____

Today I am grateful for
_____
_____
_____
_____

📍Location_____ 📅 Date_____

Weather : ☀️ 🌤️ ☁️ ⛈️ 🌧️ 🌨️
_____
_____

What I did today
_____
_____
_____
_____
_____
_____

Best thing that happened today
_____
_____
_____
_____

Funniest thing that happened today
_____
_____
_____
_____

My mood was : 😊 😍 😎 😜 😴 😭
_____
_____

Who I shared the day with
_____
_____
_____

Today I am grateful for
_____
_____
_____

📍Location_____ 📅 Date_____

Weather :- ☀️ 🌤️ ☁️ ⛈️ 🌧️ 🌨️
_____
_____

What I did today
_____
_____
_____
_____
_____

Best thing that happened today
_____
_____
_____
_____

Funniest thing that happened today
_____
_____
_____
_____

My mood was : 😊 😍 😎 😋 😴 😣
_____
_____

Who I shared the day with
_____
_____
_____

Today I am grateful for
_____
_____
_____

Location_____ Date_____

Weather : ☀ ⛅ ☁ ⛈ 🌧 🌨
_____
_____

What I did today
_____
_____
_____
_____
_____
_____

Best thing that happened today
_____
_____
_____
_____

Funniest thing that happened today
_____
_____
_____
_____

My mood was : 😊 😍 😎 😜 😴 😣
_____
_____

Who I shared the day with
_____
_____
_____

Today I am grateful for
_____
_____
_____

📍Location_____ 📅 Date_____

Weather : ☀️ ⛅ ☁️ ⛈️ 🌧️ 🌨️
_____
_____

What I did today
_____
_____
_____
_____
_____
_____

Best thing that happened today
_____
_____
_____
_____

Funniest thing that happened today
_____
_____
_____
_____

My mood was : 😊 😍 😎 😜 😤 😣

_____
_____

Who I shared the day with
_____
_____
_____
_____

Today I am grateful for
_____
_____
_____
_____

📍Location_____ 📅Date_____

Weather :- ☀️ ⛅ ☁️ ⚡ 🌧️ 🌨️
_____
_____

What I did today
_____
_____
_____
_____
_____
_____

Best thing that happened today
_____
_____
_____

Funniest thing that happened today
_____
_____

My mood was : 😊 😍 😎 😜 😴 😭
_____
_____

Who I shared the day with
_____
_____
_____

Today I am grateful for
_____
_____
_____

📍Location_____ 🗓️Date_____

Weather : ☀️ ⛅ ☁️ ⛈️ 🌧️ 🌨️
_____
_____

What I did today

_____
_____
_____
_____
_____
_____

Best thing that happened today

_____
_____
_____
_____

Funniest thing that happened today

_____
_____
_____
_____

My mood was : 😊 😍 😎 😜 😴 😣

_____
_____

Who I shared the day with

_____
_____
_____

Today I am grateful for

_____
_____
_____

📍Location_____ 🗓 Date_____

Weather : ☀️ ⛅ ☁️ ⛈️ 🌧️ 🌨️
_____
_____

What I did today
_____
_____
_____
_____
_____
_____

Best thing that happened today
_____
_____
_____
_____

Funniest thing that happened today
_____
_____
_____
_____

My mood was : 😊 😍 😎 😜 😴 😣
_____
_____

Who I shared the day with
_____
_____
_____

Today I am grateful for
_____
_____
_____

Location_____ **Date**_____

Weather : ☀ ⛅ ☁ ⛈ 🌧 🌨
_____
_____

What I did today
_____
_____
_____
_____
_____
_____

Best thing that happened today
_____
_____
_____
_____

Funniest thing that happened today
_____
_____
_____
_____

My mood was : 😊 😍 😎 😜 😤 😣
_____
_____

Who I shared the day with
_____
_____
_____

Today I am grateful for
_____
_____
_____

⊙ Location_____ 🗓 Date_____

Weather :☀ ⛅ ☁ ⛈ 🌧 🌨
_____
_____

What I did today
_____
_____
_____
_____
_____
_____

Best thing that happened today
_____
_____
_____
_____

Funniest thing that happened today
_____
_____
_____
_____

My mood was : 😊 😍 😎 😜 😒 😣
_____
_____

Who I shared the day with
_____
_____
_____

Today I am grateful for
_____
_____
_____

⚲ Location_____ 🗓 Date_____

Weather : ☀ ⛅ ☁ ⛈ 🌧 🌨
_____
_____

What I did today
_____
_____
_____
_____
_____
_____
_____

Best thing that happened today
_____
_____
_____
_____

Funniest thing that happened today
_____
_____
_____
_____

My mood was : 😊 😍 😎 😜 😴 😢
_____
_____

Who I shared the day with
_____
_____
_____

Today I am grateful for
_____
_____
_____

📍Location_____ 🗓️Date_____

Weather :- ☀️ ⛅ ☁️ ⚡ 🌧️ 🌨️
_____
_____

What I did today
_____
_____
_____
_____
_____
_____

Best thing that happened today
_____
_____
_____
_____

Funniest thing that happened today
_____
_____
_____
_____

My mood was : 😊 😍 😎 😜 😴 😫
_____
_____

Who I shared the day with
_____
_____
_____

Today I am grateful for
_____
_____
_____

📍Location_____ 📅 Date_____

Weather :- ☀ 🌤 ☁ ⛈ 🌧 🌨
_____
_____

What I did today
_____
_____
_____
_____
_____
_____

Best thing that happened today
_____
_____
_____
_____

Funniest thing that happened today
_____
_____
_____
_____

My mood was : 😊 😍 😎 😜 😴 😭
_____
_____

Who I shared the day with
_____
_____
_____

Today I am grateful for
_____
_____
_____

📍Location_____ 🗓Date_____

Weather : ☀️ 🌤 ⛅ ⛈ 🌧 🌨
_____
_____

What I did today

_____
_____
_____
_____
_____
_____

Best thing that happened today

_____
_____
_____

Funniest thing that happened today

_____
_____
_____

My mood was : 😊 😍 😎 😜 😴 😣

_____
_____

Who I shared the day with

_____
_____
_____

Today I am grateful for

_____
_____
_____

📍 Location_____ 📅 Date_____

Weather : ☀️ ⛅ ☁️ ⚡ 🌧️ 🌨️
_____
_____

What I did today
_____
_____
_____
_____
_____
_____

Best thing that happened today
_____
_____
_____

Funniest thing that happened today
_____
_____
_____

My mood was : 😊 😍 😎 😜 😴 😣
_____
_____

Who I shared the day with
_____
_____
_____

Today I am grateful for
_____
_____
_____

📍Location_____ 📅Date_____

Weather : ☀️ ⛅ ☁️ ⛈️ 🌧️ 🌨️
_____
_____

What I did today
_____
_____
_____
_____
_____
_____

Best thing that happened today
_____
_____
_____
_____

Funniest thing that happened today
_____
_____
_____
_____

My mood was : 😊 😍 😎 😜 😠 😫
_____
_____

Who I shared the day with
_____
_____
_____

Today I am grateful for
_____
_____
_____

📍Location_____ 🗓Date_____

Weather : ☀ ⛅ ☁ ⛈ 🌧 🌨
_____
_____

What I did today
_____
_____
_____
_____
_____
_____

Best thing that happened today
_____
_____
_____
_____

Funniest thing that happened today
_____
_____
_____
_____

My mood was : 😊 😍 😎 😜 😴 😭

_____
_____

Who I shared the day with
_____
_____
_____

Today I am grateful for
_____
_____
_____

📍Location_____ 🗓Date_____

Weather :☀️ ⛅ ☁️ ⚡ 🌧️ 🌨️
_____
_____

What I did today

_____
_____
_____
_____
_____
_____

Best thing that happened today

_____
_____
_____
_____

Funniest thing that happened today

_____
_____
_____
_____

My mood was : 😊 😍 😎 😜 😴 😣

_____
_____

Who I shared the day with

_____
_____
_____

Today I am grateful for

_____
_____
_____

📍Location_____ 🗓Date_____

Weather : ☀ ⛅ ☁ ⚡ 🌧 🌨
_____
_____

What I did today
_____
_____
_____
_____
_____

Best thing that happened today
_____
_____
_____

Funniest thing that happened today
_____
_____
_____

My mood was : 😊 😍 😎 😜 😴 😭
_____
_____

Who I shared the day with
_____
_____
_____

Today I am grateful for
_____
_____
_____

📍Location_____ 🗓Date_____

Weather :☀ 🌤 ☁ ⚡ 🌧 🌨
_____
_____

What I did today
_____
_____
_____
_____
_____
_____

Best thing that happened today
_____
_____
_____
_____

Funniest thing that happened today
_____
_____
_____
_____

My mood was : 😊 😍 😎 😜 😴 😣
_____
_____

Who I shared the day with
_____
_____
_____

Today I am grateful for
_____
_____
_____

📍Location_____ 📅 Date_____

Weather :☀️ ⛅ ☁️ ⚡ 🌧️ 🌨️
_____
_____

What I did today

_____
_____
_____
_____
_____
_____

Best thing that happened today

_____
_____
_____
_____

Funniest thing that happened today

_____
_____
_____
_____

My mood was : 😊 😍 😎 😜 😴 😣

_____
_____

Who I shared the day with

_____
_____
_____

Today I am grateful for

_____
_____
_____

📍Location_____ 📅Date_____

Weather :☀️ ⛅ ☁️ ⚡ 🌧️ 🌨️
_____
_____

What I did today
_____
_____
_____
_____
_____
_____

Best thing that happened today
_____
_____
_____
_____

Funniest thing that happened today
_____
_____
_____
_____

My mood was : 😊 😍 😎 😜 😴 😣
_____
_____

Who I shared the day with
_____
_____
_____

Today I am grateful for
_____
_____
_____

📍Location_____ 🗓Date_____

Weather :- ☀ ⛅ ☁ ⚡ 🌧 ❄
_____
_____

What I did today
_____
_____
_____
_____
_____
_____
_____

Best thing that happened today
_____
_____
_____
_____

Funniest thing that happened today
_____
_____
_____
_____

My mood was : 😊 😍 😎 😜 😴 😭
_____
_____

Who I shared the day with
_____
_____
_____
_____

Today I am grateful for
_____
_____
_____
_____

📍Location_____ 🗓️Date_____

Weather :☀️ 🌤️ ☁️ ⚡ 🌧️ ❄️
_____
_____

What I did today

_____
_____
_____
_____
_____

Best thing that happened today
_____
_____
_____
_____

Funniest thing that happened today
_____
_____
_____
_____

My mood was : 😊 😍 😎 😜 😴 😣
_____
_____

Who I shared the day with
_____
_____
_____

Today I am grateful for
_____
_____
_____

Made in United States
North Haven, CT
31 May 2023

37213908R00057